70 YEARS OF POPULAR MUSIC

THE TWENTIES

Part Four

Production: Sadie Cook

Music processed by Global Music Solutions, Surrey SM6 9BT

Cover design by Headline Publicity Limited

Published 1997

IMP

AM I BLUE?

Words by GRANT CLARKE
Music by HARRY AKST

BASIN STREET BLUES

Words and Music by SPENCER WILLIAMS

BECAUSE MY BABY DON'T MEAN MAYBE NOW

Words and Music by WALTER DONALDSON

Ev - 'ry - thing seems love - ly, the world is so se - rene, when
Ev - 'ry - thing is ro - sy, I feel so, so and so, when

I say things are love - ly, you know just what I mean. It
I say things are ro - sy, I know you know I know.

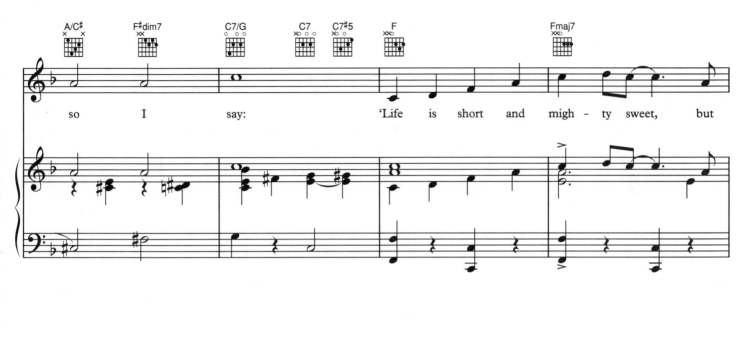

so I say: 'Life is short and might-y sweet, but

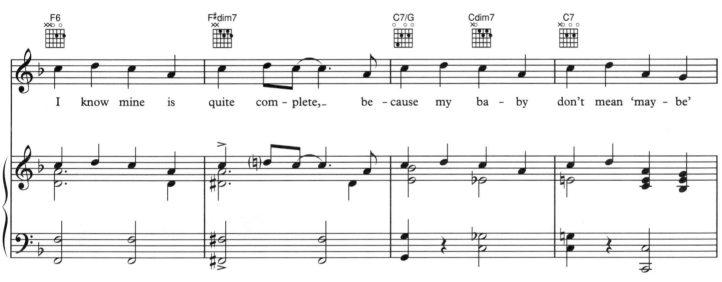

I know mine is quite com-plete,_ be-cause my ba-by don't mean 'may-be'

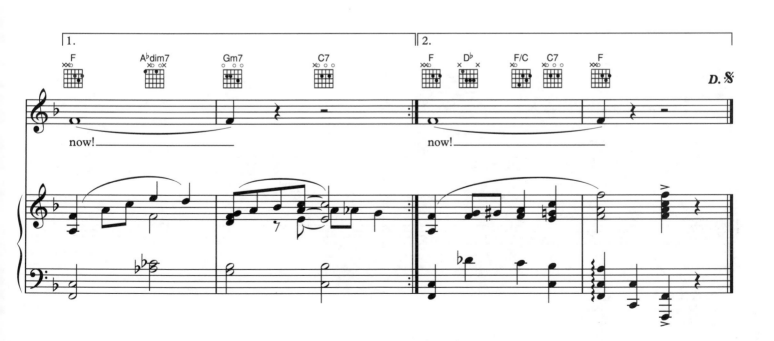

now!_____   now!_____

D. %

BUGLE CALL RAG

Words and Music by JOHN PETTIS, BILLY MEYERS
and ELMER SCHOEBEL

A CUP OF COFFEE, A SANDWICH AND YOU

Words by AL DUBIN and BILLY ROSE
Music by JOSEPH MEYER

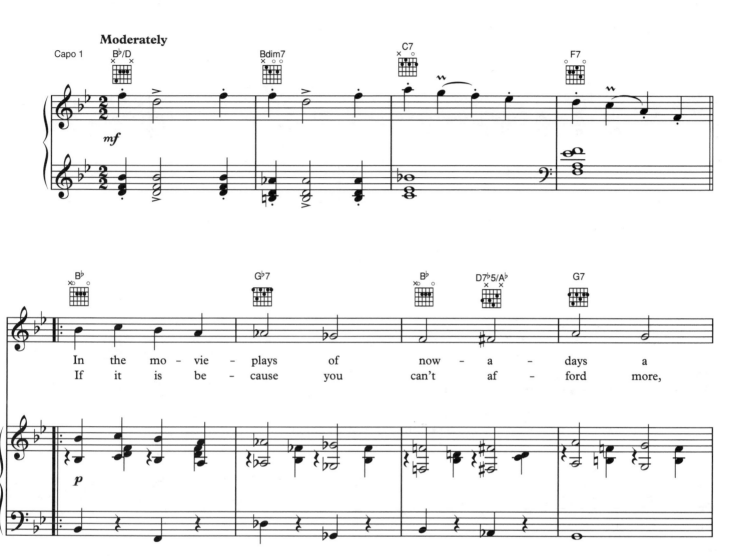

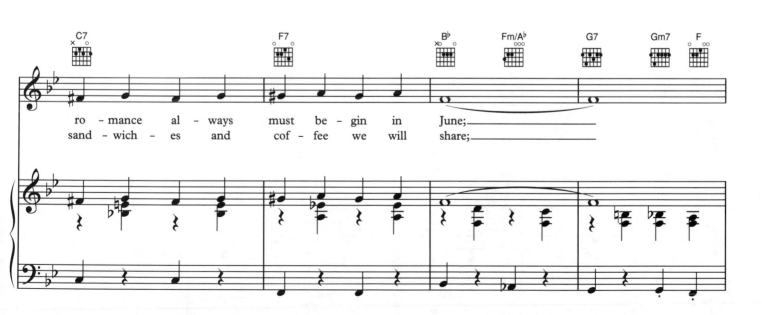

Lyrics (line 1):
In the mo-vie - plays of now - a - days a ro-mance al-ways must be-gin in June;

Lyrics (line 2):
If it is be - cause you can't af - ford more, sand-wich-es and cof-fee we will share;

Tales in ma - ga - zines have all their scenes of
But if it's to help you save and hoard more,

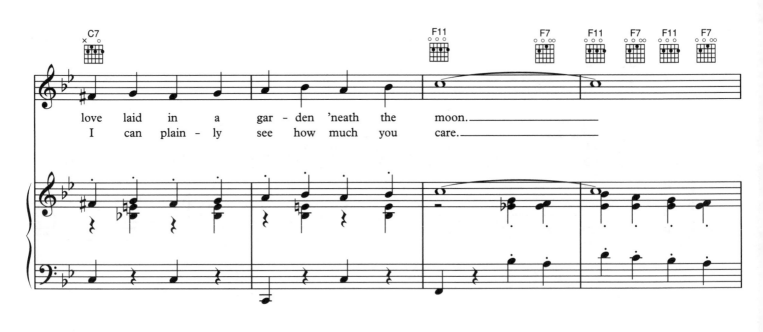

love laid in a gar - den 'neath the moon.
I can plain - ly see how much you care.

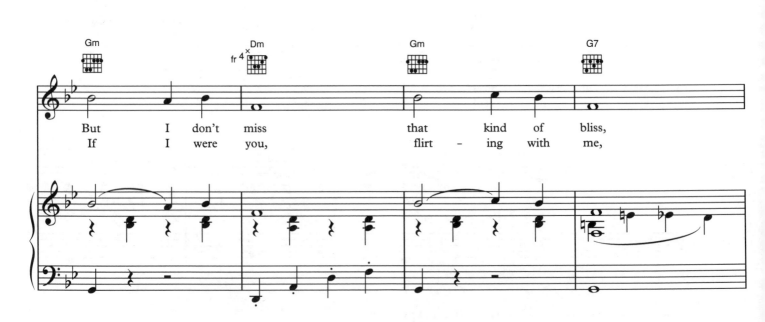

But I don't miss that kind of bliss,
If I were you, flirt - ing with me,

DELANEY'S DONKEY

Words and Music by WILLIAM HARGREAVES

De - la - ney had a don - key ev - 'ry - one ad - mired;
The mus - cle of the migh - ty, ne - ver known to flinch,
The crowd be - gan to cheer it. Raf - fer - ty, the judge,

tem - po - 'ri - ly la - zy, per - ma - nent - ly tired; a leg at ev - 'ry cor - ner
did - n't move the don - key quar - ter of an inch. De - la - ney lay ex - haust - ed,
came up to as - sist them, still it would - n't budge. The jock - ey who was rid - ing,

ba - lanc - ing   its   head,   and   a   tail   to   let   you   know   which   end   it   wan - ted   to   be   fed.
hang - ing   round   it's   throat   with   a   grip   just   like   a   Scotch - man   on   a   twen - ty   shil - ling   note.
lit - tle   John   Mac - Gee,   was   so   thor - ough - ly   dis - gust - ed   he   went   home   to   get   his   tea.

Ri - ley   sly - ly   said,   'We've   un - der - ra - ted   it.   Why   not   train   it?'
Start - er,   Cart - er,   lined   up   all   the   rest   of   'em;   when   it   saw   them,
Ha - gan,   Fa - gan,   stu - dents   of   psy - cho - lo - gy,   swore   they'd   shift   it

Then   he   took   a   rag,   rubbed   it,   scrubbed   it,   oiled   and   em - bro - ca - ted   it,
it   was   wil - ling   then.   Raced   up,   braced   up,   rea - dy   for   the   best   of   'em;   they
with   some   dy - na - mite;   bought   it,   brought   it,   then   with - out   a - po - lo - gy   the

Town Hall down. The don-key was eye-ing them, o-pen-ly de-fy-ing them,
laughed 'Hee - Haw!' The whigs and con-ser-va-tives, ra-di-cal su-per-la-tives,
life guards too. They seized it and har-ried it, picked it up and car-ried it,

wink - ing, blink - ing twist - ing out of place, Ri - ley re-vers-ing it,
Lib - 'rals, tor - ies, hur - ried to the place, stood there in u - ni - ty,
cheered it, steered it, to the win - ning place. Book - ies all drew a -side

ev - 'ry - bo - dy curs - ing it, the day De - la - ney's don - key ran the half - mile race.
help - ing the com - mu - ni - ty to push De - la - ney's don - key in the half - mile race.
and com - mit - ted su - i - cide be - cause De - la - ney's don - key won the half - mile race.

D.C.

DOWN YONDER

Words and Music by L WOLFE GILBERT

DRINKING SONG

Words by DOROTHY DONNELLY
Music by SIGMUND ROMBERG

Drink! Drink! Drink! To
Drink! Drink! Drink! To

eyes that are bright as stars when they're shin-ing on me!
arms that are white as and warm as a rose in the sun!

Drink! Drink! Drink! To lips that are red and
Drink! Drink! Drink! To hearts that will love one,

sweet as the fruit on the tree! Here's a hope that those
on - ly when I am the one! Here's a hope that those

mp *espressivo e meno mosso*

bright eyes will shine lov - ing - ly, long - ing - ly, soon in - to mine!
soft arms will twine ten - der - ly, trust - ing - ly, soon a - round mine!

poco allarg.

FIVE FOOT TWO, EYES OF BLUE
(HAS ANYBODY SEEN MY GIRL?)

Words by JOE YOUNG and SAM LEWIS
Music by RAY HENDERSON

DOES THE SPEARMINT LOSE ITS FLAVOUR (ON THE BEDPOST OVERNIGHT)?

Words by BILLY ROSE and MARTY BLOOM
Music by ERNEST BREUER

HALFWAY DOWN THE STAIRS

Words by A. A. MILNE
Music by HOWARD FRASER-SIMSON

HOW LONG HAS THIS BEEN GOING ON?

Music and Lyrics by GEORGE GERSHWIN and IRA GERSHWIN

Bill: As a tot, when I trot - ted in lit - tle vel - vet pant - ies,_____
Mary: 'Neath the stars at ba - zaars of - ten I've had to ca - ress men,_____

I was kissed by my sis - ters, my cou - sins and my aunt - ies._____
Five or ten dol - lars then I'd col - lect from all those yes - men.

I WISH I COULD SHIMMY LIKE MY SISTER KATE

Words and Music by ARMAND J PIRON

I WONDER WHERE MY BABY IS TONIGHT

Words by GUS KAHN
Music by WALTER DONALDSON

I burned up ev-'ry let-ter, and thought that I'd feel bet-ter;
I know she said 'for-get me', and so I wish she'd let me;

I put a-way her pic-ture too.
why does she haunt me night and day?

(I'LL BUILD A) STAIRWAY TO PARADISE

Music and Lyrics by GEORGE GERSHWIN, BUDDY DE SYLVA
and ARTHUR FRANCIS

All you preach-ers who de-light in slam-ming the
Ev - 'ry new step helps a bit; but a-ny old

danc-ing teach-ers, let me tell you there are a lot of fea-tures
kind of two-step does as well. It don't mat-ter what step you step,

I'M JUST WILD ABOUT HARRY

Words and Music by NOBLE SISSLE and EUBIE BLAKE

There's just one fel - low for me in this world,___
There are some fel - lows that like all the girls,___

Har - ry's his name,___ that's what I claim___ why
I mean the vamps,___ with cru - el lamps___ but

I'M NOBODY'S BABY

Words and Music by BENNY DAVIS, MILTON AGER
and LESTER SANTLY

I'VE NEVER SEEN A STRAIGHT BANANA

Words and Music by TED WAITE

INDIAN LOVE CALL

Words by OTTO HARBACH and OSCAR HAMMERSTEIN II
Music by RUDOLF FRIML

JUST A GIGOLO

Words and Music by JULIUS BRAMMER, LEONELLO CASUCCI
and IRVING CAESAR

K-RA-ZY FOR YOU

Music and Lyrics by GEORGE GERSHWIN and IRA GERSHWIN

THE LAZIEST GAL IN TOWN

Words and Music by COLE PORTER

LET'S MISBEHAVE

Words and Music by COLE PORTER

MORE THAN YOU KNOW

Words by BILLY ROSE and EDWARD ELISCU
Music by VINCENT YOUMANS

LET'S DO IT (LET'S FALL IN LOVE)

Words and Music by COLE PORTER
Additional Words by NOËL COWARD

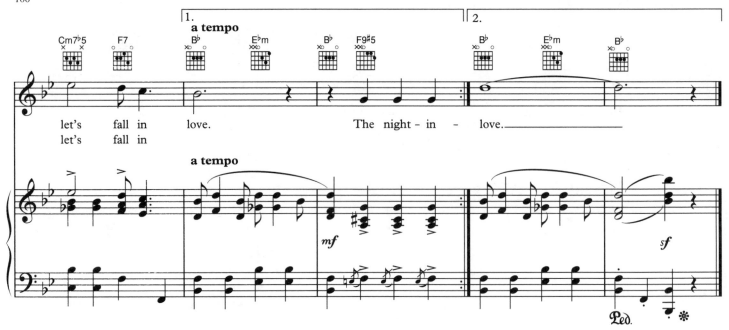

let's   fall in   love.   The night - in - love.
let's   fall in

Verse 1:

Mr Irving Berlin
Often emphasizes sin
In a charming way
Mr Coward we know
Wrote a song or two to show
Sex was here to stay
Richard Rodgers it's true
Takes a more romantic view
Of that sly biological urge
But it really was Cole
Who contrived to make the whole
Thing merge

Verse 2:

In the Spring of the year
Inhibitions disappear
And our hearts beat high
We had better face the facts
Every gland that overacts
Has an alibi
For each bird and each bee
Each slap-happy sappy tree
Each temptation that lures us along
Is just nature elle-même
Merely singing us the same
Old song

Refrain 1:

He said that Belgians and Dutch do it
Even Hildegarde and Hutch do it
Let's do it, let's fall in love
Monkeys whenever you look do it
Aly Khan and King Farouk do it
Let's do it, let's fall in love
The most recherché cocottes do it
In a luxury flat
Locks, Dunns and Scotts do it
At the drop of a hat
Excited spinsters in spas do it
Duchesses when opening bazaars do it
Let's do it, let's fall in love

Refrain 3:

Girls from the R.A.D.A. do it
B.B.C. announcers may do it
Let's do it, let's fall in love
The Ballet Russe to a man do it
Alfred Lunt and Lynn Fontanne do it
Let's do it, let's fall in love
My kith and kin, more or less, do it
Every uncle and aunt
But I confess to it
I've one cousin who can't
Critics as sour as quince do it
Even Emile Littler and Prince do it
Let's do it, let's fall in love

Refrain 2:

Our leading writers in swarms do it
Somerset and all the Maughams do it
Let's do it, let's fall in love
The Brontës felt that they must do it
Mrs Humphry Ward could just do it
Let's do it, let's fall in love
Anouilh and Sartre - God knows why - do it
As a sort of curse
Eliot and Fry do it
But they do it in verse
Some mystics, as a routine do it
Even Evelyn Waugh and Graham Greene do it
Let's do it, let's fall in love

Refrain 4:

The House of Commons en bloc do it
Civil servants by the clock do it
Let's do it, let's fall in love
Deacons who've done it before do it
Minor canons with a roar do it
Let's do it, let's fall in love
Some rather rorty old rips do it
When they get a bit tight
Government Whips do it
If it takes them all night
Old mountain goats in ravines do it
Probably we'll live to see machines do it
Let's do it, let's fall in love

MUSKRAT RAMBLE

Words by RAY GILBERT
Music by EDWARD ORY

THE ONE I LOVE BELONGS TO SOMEBODY ELSE

Words by GUS KAHN
Music by ISHAM JONES

I'm un - hap - py, so un - hap - py, for I can see
I keep try - ing, I keep try - ing to stay a - way

the one I love
it can't be done

don't care for
one sin - gle

ROSE OF THE RIO GRANDE

Words by EDGAR LESLIE
Music by HARRY WARREN and ROSS GORMAN

110

NOBODY KNOWS YOU
WHEN YOU'RE DOWN AND OUT

Words and Music by JIMMIE COX

Once I lived the life of a mil-lion-aire.__ Spend-ing my mon-ey, I didn't care. I car-ried my friends out for a good time__ buy-ing boot-leg lik-ker,__ cham-pagne and wine.__ When I be-gan to fall__ so slow__ I

A SHIP WITHOUT A SAIL

Words by LORENZ HART
Music by RICHARD RODGERS

He: I don't know what day it is, or if it's dark or fair; Some-
She: When love leaves you all a - lone, you're liv - ing in the past;

-how, that's just the way it is, and I don't real - ly
Then you feel so small a - lone, and oh! The world seems

THE RUNAWAY TRAIN

Words by ROBERT E MASSEY
Music by CARSON ROBISON

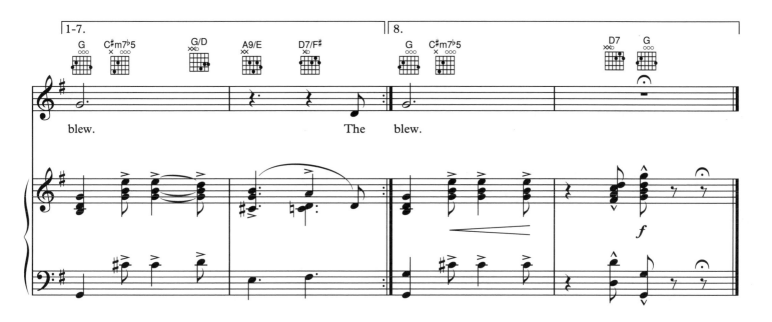

blew.   The blew.

Chorus 2:

The engineer said the train must halt
And she blew - she blew
The engineer said the train must halt
And she blew - she blew
The engineer said the train must halt
He said it was all the fireman's fault
And she blew, blew, blew, blew, blew

Chorus 3:

The fireman said he rang the bell
And she blew - she blew
The fireman said he rang the bell
And she blew - she blew
The fireman said he rang the bell
The engineer said you did like 'FUN'
And she blew, blew, blew, blew, blew

Chorus 4:

The porter got an awful fright
And she blew- she blew
The porter got an awful fright
And she blew - she blew
The porter got an awful fright
He got so scared that he turned white
And she blew, blew, blew, blew, blew

Chorus 5:

A mule was standing in the way
And she blew - she blew
A mule was standing in the way
And she blew - she blew
A mule was standing in the way
And all they found was just his bray
And she blew, blew, blew, blew, blew

Chorus 6:

A drummer sat in the parlour car
And she blew - she blew
A drummer sat in the parlour car
And she blew - she blew
A drummer sat in the parlour car
And he nearly swallowed a fat cigar
And she blew, blew, blew, blew, blew

Chorus 7:

The conductor said there'd be a wreck
And she blew - she blew
The conductor said there'd be a wreck
And she blew - she blew
The conductor said there'd be a wreck
And he felt the chills run up his neck
And she blew, blew, blew, blew, blew

Chorus 8:

The runaway train went over the hill
And she blew - she blew
The runaway train went over the hill
And she blew - she blew
The runaway train went over the hill
And the last we heard she was going still
And she blew, blew, blew, blew, blew

SAY IT WITH MUSIC

Words and Music by IRVING BERLIN

SHAKING THE BLUES AWAY

Words and Music by IRVING BERLIN

'TAIN'T NOBODY'S BIZ-NESS IF I DO

Words and Music by PORTER GRAINGER and EVERETT ROBBINS

THEY'RE CHANGING GUARD AT BUCKINGHAM PALACE

Words by A.A. MILNE
Music by HAROLD FRASER-SIMSON

In March time (very martial)

WHAT'LL I DO?

Words and Music by IRVING BERLIN

TOOT TOOT TOOTSIE, GOO'BYE

Words and Music by GUS KAHN, ERNIE ERDMAN,
DAN RUSSO and TED FIORITO

you don't get a let-ter then you'll know I'm in jail,——

Tut, tut, Toot-sie, don't cry, Toot, Toot,

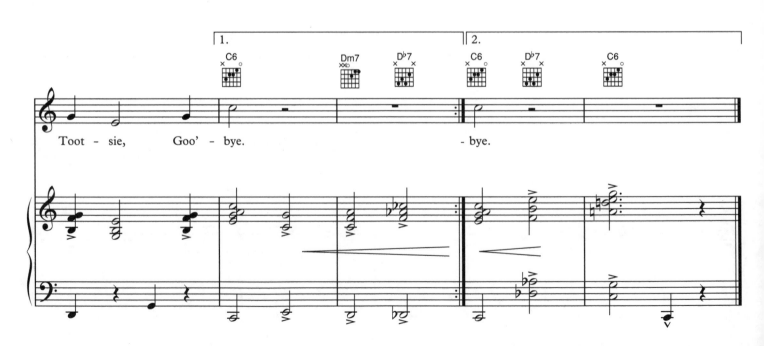

Toot-sie, Goo'-bye. -bye.

YES! WE HAVE NO BANANAS

Words and Music by FRANK SILVER and IRVING CONN

There's a fruit store on our street, it's run by a Greek,
Bus-'ness got so good with him he wrote home to say,

and he keeps good
'Send me Pete and

things to eat but you should hear him speak.
Nick and Jim, I need help right a - way'.

When you ask him a - ny -thing
When he got them in the store

WHEN MY BABY SMILES AT ME

Words by TED LEWIS and ANDREW B STERLING
Music by BILL MUNRO

WITHOUT A SONG

Words by BILLY ROSE and EDWARD ELISCU
Music by VINCENT YOUMANS

70 YEARS OF POPULAR MUSIC

The 70 Years of Popular Music is a collection of 31 books, each containing 40 of your favourite hits from the beginning of the 1900s to the present day. The music is arranged for piano with lyrics and guitar chord boxes included.

1900-1920
Order Ref: 16407
Including: After You've Gone;
The Floral Dance;
I'm Forever Blowing Bubbles; Swanee

The Twenties Part One
Order Ref: 09906
Including: April Showers;
Crazy Rhythm;
Makin' Whoopee!; Tea For Two;
Yes Sir That's My Baby

The Twenties Part Two
Order Ref: 17713
Including: Ain't Misbehavin';
The Charleston;
My Blue Heaven; Side By Side;
Singin' In The Rain

The Twenties Part Three
Order Ref: 2273A
Including: Ain't She Sweet;
Baby Face; Don't Bring Lulu;
It Had To Be You;
Who's Sorry Now

The Twenties Part Four
Order Ref: 5620A
Including: Basin St Blues;
Indian Love Call;
Let's Do It (Let's Fall In Love);
Without A Song

The Thirties Part One
Order Ref: 09907
Including: All Of Me; A Foggy Day;
I Only Have Eyes For You;
September Song;
Smoke Gets In Your Eyes

The Thirties Part Two
Order Ref: 17714
Including: About A Quarter To Nine;
Blue Moon; The Glory Of Love;
Moonlight Serenade;
Over The Rainbow; Stardust

The Thirties Part Three
Order Ref: 2274A
Including: Begin The Beguine;
A Fine Romance;
Lazy Bones; My Funny Valentine;
Stormy Weather

The Thirties Part Four
Order Ref: 5621A
Including: But Not For Me;
Georgia On My Mind;
Jeepers Creepers;
My Baby Just Cares For Me

The Forties Part One
Order Ref: 09908
Including: Almost Like Being
In Love; Blueberry Hill; Let There Be Love;
My Foolish Heart; Tenderly

The Forties Part Two
Order Ref: 17715
Including: Don't Get Around Much Any
More; I Remember You; Mona Lisa;
That Old Black Magic

The Forties Part Three
Order Ref: 2275A
Including: Busy Doin' Nothing;
Stella By Starlight; Swinging On A Star;
You Make Me Feel So Young

The Forties Part Four
Order Ref: 5622A
Including: Anything You Can Do;
Choo Choo Ch'Boogie; Route 66;
Tico-Tico (Tico-Tico No Fuba)

The Fifties Part One
Order Ref: 09909
Including: Autumn Leaves; Diana;
The Green Door;
I Could Have Danced All Night;
When I Fall In Love

The Fifties Part Two
Order Ref: 17305
Including: All The Way; Cry Me A River;
High Hopes; La Bamba; Living Doll;
Only Sixteen; Volare

The Fifties Part Three
Order Ref: 2276A
Including: Come Fly With Me; I Love Paris;
Magic Moments; Mister Sandman; Misty;
Sing A Rainbow

The Fifties Part Four
Order Ref: 5623A
Including: Ain't That A Shame;
Book Of Love; Heartbreak Hotel;
Island In The Sun; Sisters; Smile

The Sixties Part One
Order Ref 09910
Including: Alfie; Congratulations;
I'm A Believer; Moon River; Puppet
On A String; Try To Remember

The Sixties Part Two
Order Ref: 17306
Including: Anyone Who Had A Heart;
Blowin' In The Wind; A Groovy Kind Of
Love; The Loco-motion

The Sixties Part Three
Order Ref: 3117A
Including: Apache; Black Is Black; C'Mon
Everybody; Everlasting Love;
Leader Of The Pack

The Sixties Part Four
Order Ref: 5624A
Including: Baby Love;
California Girls; Itchycoo Park; Mustang
Sally; Sugar Sugar; Wild Thing; Young Girl

The Seventies Part One
Order Ref: 09911
Including: Baker Street;
Don't Give Up On Us;
Hi Ho Silver Lining; If; Mandy;
Music; When I Need You

The Seventies Part Two
Order Ref: 17307
Including: Chanson D'Amour; Chiquitita;
Diamonds Are Forever; Isn't She Lovely
Jolene; Lost In France

The Seventies Part Three
Order Ref: 3118A
Including: Annie's Song; Easy;
Hotel California; I Will Survive;
Killer Queen; With You I'm Born Again

The Seventies Part Four
Order Ref: 5625A
Including: Ain't No Sunshine;
Boogie Wonderland; Dancing Queen;
Lady Marmalade; Top Of The World

The Eighties Part One
Order Ref: 16005
Including: Ben; Endless Love; It's My Tur
Let's Hear It For The Boy; Move Close
We've Got Tonight

The Eighties Part Two
Order Ref: 16966
Including: Axel F; Coming Around Again
Like A Virgin; Nikita; Separate Lives;
Take My Breath Away

The Eighties Part Three
Order Ref: 3119A
Including: Anything For You;
Being With You; Careless Whisper;
Come On Eileen; Tainted Love

The Eighties Part Four
Order Ref: 5626A
Including: Breakout;
Everything Must Change; Kids In Amer
Lady In Red; Missing You; Superwoman

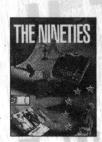

The Nineties Part One
Order Ref: 2277A
Including: All Woman; Get Here;
Heal The World; I Will Always Love You
Promise Me; Sacrifice

The Nineties Part Two
Order Ref: 5627A
Including: All I Wanna Do; Breathe Again
Don't Speak; Love Shack; Mmmbop;
Think Twice; Older

The 70 Years of Popular Music Series is available from all good music shops.

International Music Publications Limited
Southend Road, Woodford Green, Essex IG8 8HN, England
Tel: 0181 551 6131 Fax: 0181 551 9121 e-mail: IMP@dial.pipex.com